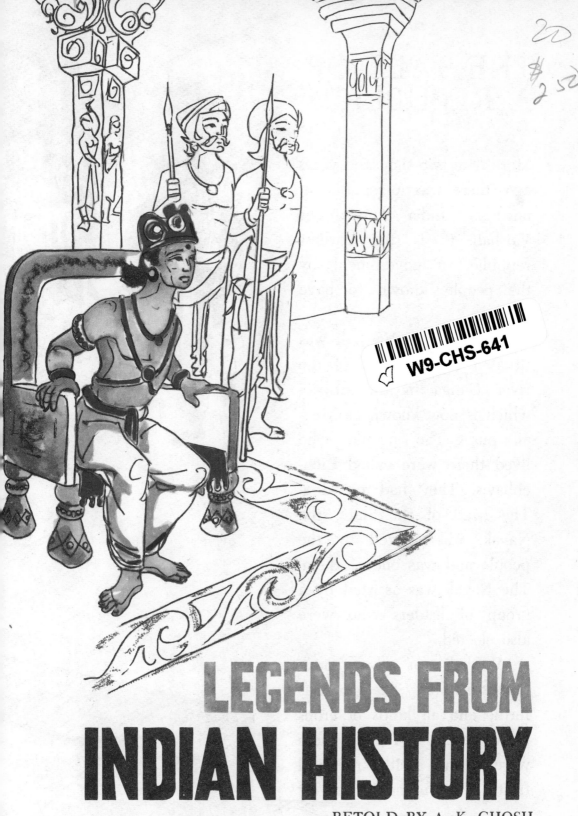

LEGENDS FROM
INDIAN HISTORY

RETOLD BY A. K. GHOSH

ILLUSTRATED BY DEBABRATA MUKERJI

THE TALE OF A REPUBLIC

More than two thousand years ago, there was a republic in northern India known as Vaishali. It is the earliest republic, or government by the people, known to have existed.

The State of Vaishali was situated on the bank of the river Ganga in the district which is now known as Muzaffarpur. The people who lived there were called Lichchhavis. They had no king. The head of the State, the Nayak, was elected by the people and was one of them. The Nayak was assisted by a group of leaders who were also elected.

Vaishali was a very prosperous country. The land was fertile and all kinds of crops grew there. Trees there were many, with plentiful fruits. The numerous rivers

and brooks supplied the people with cool, clear water. The people were happy, for they had everything they needed.

The capital of the State was the city of Vaishali. It was said that this city had been founded by a prince named Vaishal, who was the son of a great king called Ikshvaku.

Vaishali was a large and beautiful city, twenty miles in circumference; it was protected all round by a high, strong wall. There were only three gates in the wall, and they were well guarded. Inside the city there were beautiful houses as large as palaces and with domes of gold. Other houses had silver minarets, and yet others had roofs of copper. On the whole the Lichchhavi's republic was very rich and prosperous.

The people of Vaishali were noble and great. They were kind and friendly. Unity was their strength. They made their own laws which everyone obeyed. They were so strong, brave, and united that no other country dared to attack them.

The kings of neighbouring countries were jealous of this happy republic, and they waited for an opportunity to conquer it and enslave the people. But the people of Vaishali were always alert and ready to meet any challenge. At various important places war drums were kept and from time to time the drums were sounded. Hearing the drums, the people gathered at once, prepared for battle. This was an exercise to test the people's alertness.

On the other side of the Ganga was the kingdom of Magadha. In the fourth century B.C. the Emperor of Magadha was Ajatashatru. He

founded the great city of Pataliputra which is now known as Patna. Ajatashatru was a powerful king, but he was not a kind man. It was said that he was so impatient that he killed his own father, Bimbisara, so that he could himself ascend the throne.

Ajatashatru did not like Vaishali to remain independent. He wanted to take possession of it. He would have liked to fight the Lichchhavis and conquer them, but he knew their strength and he knew their wonderful unity; so he did not dare to take the risk.

Ajatashatru had a vicious and crafty minister named Vasyakar. This minister knew the king's desire to conquer Vaishali and one day he spoke to him about it.

"Your Majesty,"

said Vasyakar, "I know what you feel about Vaishali. If you have faith in me, I shall get Vaishali for Magadha."

"How?" asked the king. "How can you get Vaishali for me?"

"This is my plan," replied the minister. "You must pretend that I have displeased you. You will publicly disgrace me and banish me from your kingdom. Then, just leave the rest to me. I shall give you a signal when to attack the Lichchhavis, and then Vaishali will be yours."

The king saw that Vasyakar had thought of a clever plan, and he wanted to help him to carry it out. So he ordered Vasyakar to be banished from the country, as he desired.

Vasyakar's head was shaved, his face was painted black,

and he was made to sit on a donkey and driven out of Pataliputra.

Vasyakar crossed the river Ganga and escaped to Vaishali. When he reached there he told the people that the Emperor of Magadha was displeased with him and had banished him and he had now come to take refuge in Vaishali.

The Lichchhavis were simple and generous people. They believed all that Vasyakar told them. They gave him shelter and they also gave him work to do in an important position. Vasyakar was very intelligent and he worked hard. He rose higher and higher in rank and soon became the Chief Justice of Vaishali.

Vasyakar was now well known. He moved freely among the people, and he was gentle and courteous to all. They liked him and trusted him.

It gave him great satisfaction to see that he now had the people's full confidence. He had completed the first step of his plan, and had won his first victory.

Now he entered upon the second part of his plan. He began to play one man against another so that they became enemies. Gradually, he cleverly introduced the poison of disunity and enmity among the people of Vaishali. They formed groups and parties. Rivalry grew. And in a few months the unity which had been the strength of the Republic of Vaishali was broken.

Vasyakar was happy. He felt that he was nearing his goal. He wanted to find out how far he had progressed, so he decided to put the people to the test. One day he ordered the war drums to be sounded. Few people took any notice of the call. Vasyakar was pleased. He knew

that the hour had come. He sent a spy to Ajatashatru, inviting him to invade Vaishali.

Ajatashatru was waiting for this. With a large army he crossed the Ganga at night and was soon at the gates of the

city of Vaishali. Vasyakar had one of the gates opened, and Ajatashatru's army entered the Republic of Vaishali.

The war drums were sounded, but few were prepared to fight. Vaishali fell.

King Ajatashatru, seated in a golden chariot drawn by eight white horses, entered Vaishali and was welcomed by his own army, for they had already taken full possession of the city.

Thus Ajatashatru conquered the Republic of Vaishali and added it to the Magadha empire. He introduced his taxes and imposed his laws. He made the Lichchhavis his slaves.

A PRINCE'S REVENGE

In India, during the lifetime of the Buddha, there was a famous kingdom called Kosala. Its capital was Sravasti, a great city on the banks of the river Rapti. Prasenajit was the King of Kosala. He was a great devotee of the Buddha. He had constructed many ashramas and Buddhist shrines, and the Buddha himself used to visit them. Many famous scriptures were prepared in these places. Moreover, King Prasenajit also made arrangements to feed five hundred monks every day in his palace.

One day King Prasenajit came to know that none of the

monks ate their food at the palace. Instead, they took it all away to the houses of their relatives and friends and ate it there. The king was surprised at this and he made enquiries to find out the reason why the monks did not eat at his palace.

He was told that all the monks were Sakyas, of the same clan as the Buddha. They considered themselves socially

superior to the people of the Kosala royal family, and they always ate their food with the people of their own class.

This set King Prasenajit thinking.

"If I were to marry a daughter of one of the Sakyas and make her my chief queen," he thought to himself, "then, because of this relationship, the monks would consider my social status to be the same as theirs."

So King Prasenajit wanted to marry a Sakya princess. But he did not know how to proceed in the matter. One day he went out hunting. While chasing a wild animal, he was somehow separated from his companions. Finding

himself alone, he rode on and when he had travelled a long distance he found he had entered the Sakya kingdom.

When the Sakyas came to know that King Prasenajit had come to their kingdom they went to meet him and received him with great respect and honour. The king was happy to find them so very hospitable. He stayed with them for a few days as their guest in Kapilavastu, the Sakya capital.

During his stay, he expressed his desire to marry one of their princesses.

The Sakyas were surprised. They never expected such an approach from King Prasenajit. And they did not want a girl of royal Sakya blood to marry him. But Sakya was a dependant State under Kosala, and they could not refuse.

So the Sakyas met to discuss the matter. Mahanama, the head of the Sakyas, said that he would handle the matter in such a way that the king would be pleased.

"I have a daughter, Vasavi by name," he explained, "whose mother is a slave-woman. The girl is now sixteen and is very beautiful. We shall give her to the Kosala king as one who was born of our clan."

So the Sakyas gave the slave-woman's daughter in marriage to King Prasenajit, saying that she was a Sakya princess.

The king returned to his kingdom with his new wife

and there were great celebrations in the city in her honour.

In the evening King Prasenajit saw his young bride weeping.

"What is the cause of this unhappiness?" he asked.

"The Sakyas have cheated you," she said. "They did

not want one of their girls to marry you. So they gave me to you as a Sakya princess. I am the daughter of Mahanama, the Sakya chief, not by his queen but by a slave-woman."

King Prasenajit was shocked and he wanted to take revenge on the Sakyas, but on second thoughts he forgave them. He embraced his wife and consoled her. But Vasavi could not forget. She hated the Sakyas for deceiving such a noble man. The more King Prasenajit loved her, the more she hated the Sakyas.

Time passed, and a son was born to Vasavi. He grew up to be a handsome, healthy young man. His name was Birudhak. He often asked his mother about his grandfather and grandmother. He wanted to know why he was not allowed to go and visit them, as was the custom.

His mother told him that his grandfather was the Sakya king and he lived far, far away. But Birudhak kept on asking her for permission to go and visit his grandparents. At last Vasavi could not put him off any longer and she allowed him to visit the Sakya king. She sent word to her father that her son was coming to visit him.

When the Sakyas heard that the son of the King of Kosala was arriving they were not happy. They did not like to receive and honour the son of a slave-girl. Nevertheless they had to treat him with all courtesy.

When the prince arrived at the council hall of the Sakyas he was received with all due formality, but there was no warmth in the welcome. Birudhak felt that he was not receiving the attention and affection due to him from his grandfather and the people. Yet he could not understand the cause of their coldness.

Birudhak spent some days with his grandfather and then set out on his return journey. One of his escorts found that he had left his spear behind and he went back to fetch it. Entering the council hall which they had just left, the escort was surprised to see a slave-woman washing the seat which Birudhak had occupied. He asked her the reason for this.

"This is the place where the son of a slave sat. His mother, Vasavi, was a slave-woman, therefore the seat must be washed," the slave-woman replied.

The escort went and reported the matter to the prince. Birudhak was very annoyed. As soon as he reached home he asked his mother the meaning of what the Sakya slave-woman had said.

"Yes," replied his mother. "It is true. I am the daughter of a slave, but my father is Mahanama, the chief of the Sakyas. And the Sakyas cheated your father by

marrying me to him, for they told him that I was a princess of the royal blood."

"I am going to teach the Sakyas a good lesson for what they have done to my father," Birudhak shouted.

Years passed. Prince Birudhak became the king when his father died. He did not forget his vow. He went with

a mighty army to destroy the Sakyas. Birudhak fought the Sakyas with such determination that all the Sakyas were killed and the Sakya capital, Kapilavastu, was razed to the ground.

But Birudhak never returned to Sravasti. Ajatashatru the Emperor of Magadha, attacked Kosala. Kosala fell and was absorbed into the powerful Magadha empire.

The beautiful city of Sravasti was destroyed, never to rise again.

YASODHARMAN

Those were dark days for India. Huns from Central Asia were invading India in wave after wave. They came and fought their way through all opposition. Wherever they

went they killed and plundered, and the once-famous Gupta empire fell and was broken up.

Toramana, the Hun leader, established himself in Malwa and the Malwa king withdrew to the small kingdom of Mandsour. Toramana was succeeded by his son, Mihiragula. He was more cruel and more wicked than his father.

The king of Malwa had a son named Yasodharman. He was a young man of high qualities and he was also very ambitious. He wanted to regain the lost kingdom. He

dreamt of establishing a vast empire where his people would live happily and peacefully.

Yasodharman was only sixteen and he was restless. He wanted to see the country and know the people. He wanted to travel and find out for himself how the people lived, and what they thought about the rulers. He wanted to know how far he could depend upon them.

Taking permission from his father, Yasodharman, with a few close friends, set out on a long journey. They were all riding their best horses. They passed through many villages and cities. They went through thick jungles, crossed over mountains, and swam across turbulent rivers. They some-

times stayed with poor people
as unknown travellers. And
sometimes they were entertained by kings. They had at
times to fight with robbers
and at other times engaged
in small battles.

One day they were passing
through a dense forest when
the prince saw a wild boar
which he started chasing.
The wild boar ran so fast
that the prince was sepa-
rated from his friends. It was
a hot day. The prince was
tired and thirsty after the chase
and he looked around for
water. But he could not find
any, so he rode on.

At last he saw a river, its
water gushing down with great
force from the high moun-
tains. The prince was so tired

and thirsty that with joy he ran into the river. But the current was very strong and he lost his balance and was carried down-stream. He tried hard to swim ashore but he was helpless against the strong current. He feared he would be drowned.

Standing on a rock, a girl was filling her vessel. She saw the drowning prince struggling in the water. As Yasodharman passed near her, she caught hold of his clothing and, using all her strength, dragged him ashore. The prince was by now unconscious, but the girl nursed him and gradually he returned to his senses.

The prince opened his eyes and looked at the girl who had saved his life.

"Who are you? What is your name?" he asked.

"Mallika is my name," she said. "I stay near here with my father who is a priest."

Yasodharman felt very grateful. "You have saved my life," he said. "Money cannot repay you for what you have done, nor even a kingdom either. I am a prince. Will you marry me?"

Without blushing, the beautiful girl said, "You are a

kshatriya and I am a brahmin
girl. Your business is warfare.
My father is a devoted brahmin, and he is old. I cannot
marry you. You must forgive
me.

" It is my good fortune that
I was able to help you," she
continued. " Consider me as
your sister who has only done
her duty. I want nothing
from you for having done my
duty."

Yasodharman was very
pleased with this reply.

" Very well, you are my
sister," he said. " But promise
me one thing. If ever you are
in difficulty you will remember me. If I can do some-
thing for you, at any time, I
shall feel most grateful."

The prince then took a
diamond ring from his finger
and gave it to Mallika.

" Keep this ring with you,"
he said. " Whenever you need
my help, send it to me. I shall
be with you as soon as I can."

Mallika smiled and took

the ring as a remembrance from her prince brother.

Years passed. Mallika was married and went to live in Mathura. The Hun leader, Mihiragula, was performing all kinds of atrocities in the country and there was hardly anyone to stop him.

There came a day when he attacked Mathura and he began to plunder the city. His soldiers captured Mallika, her husband, and their children. The commander of the Hun army promised to release them if Mallika's son would join his army and if her daughter would marry a Hun. But Mallika and her husband would not agree to this proposal and they were put in prison. They passed many painful days. Mallika prayed and prayed for help. Then she thought of the boyish face of Yasodharman and she remembered his promise. Could her prince brother help her now? Would he still remember her?

Would he recall his promise if he saw his diamond ring? Mallika wished that she could inform him. But how could she send a message? Who would carry the ring to him?

It so happened that a young Hun soldier had reason to be very grateful to Mallika. He had been seriously wounded and Mallika had treated him and saved his life. She had learnt from her father how to heal wounds. Now this soldier used to bring fruit to Mallika and her husband and it was this that kept them alive.

Mallika requested this soldier to carry the ring to Yasodharman. At first he said he was afraid to do anything of that kind. But Mallika entreated him again and again, and at last he agreed to go.

At that time Yasodharman was one of the few kings who were independent and had powerful armies. Many of the kings had lost their thrones and their countries. It was want of unity among the Indian rulers that made it possible for the Huns to become very powerful. When the Huns attacked one kingdom, the rulers of other kingdoms either kept aloof or helped the Huns in their attack. Many unfortunate kings approached Yasodharman for help in regaining their kingdoms. But Yasodharman was not sure of getting any help from those rulers and so he did not want to start a war against the Huns.

One day many rulers and the representatives of other kings were all pleading with Yasodharman to put a stop to the ambitions of the notorious king of the Huns. Again Yasodharman was not willing to take the risk of a war. He told them that their disunity was the cause of their ruin and now they only went to him for help in their difficulties. He

assured them that he would
certainly take steps to defeat
the Huns but the time had
not yet come.

Just then a servant came in
and announced the arrival of
a Hun soldier. Yasodharman
was surprised at the Hun's
visit but ordered him to be
brought in. The Hun soldier
came in, bowed, and gave
Yasodharman the ring which
Mallika had given him. The
soldier told him that the lady
who had sent the ring was
in prison.

Yasodharman looked at the
ring. He remembered it. And
he remembered that it was
because of Mallika that he
was alive and on the throne.
He had to go to her help.

Yasodharman stood up.
He declared that he was ready
to start war on the Huns. He
ordered his army to be ready
and soon he was on his way
to the battlefield. Many kings
joined him.

There was a great battle

between the Huns and Yasodharman's forces. The Huns
were completely defeated

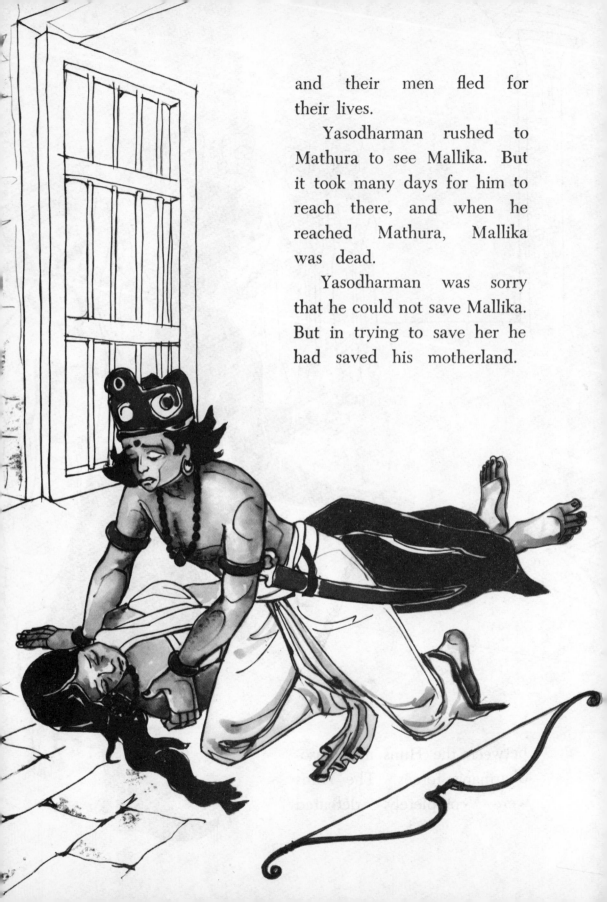

and their men fled for their lives.

Yasodharman rushed to Mathura to see Mallika. But it took many days for him to reach there, and when he reached Mathura, Mallika was dead.

Yasodharman was sorry that he could not save Mallika. But in trying to save her he had saved his motherland.

PRITHVIRAJ CHAUHAN

Prithviraj Chauhan was the last Hindu king to rule at Delhi.
He was a great ruler, and the people loved him. There are
many stories of his great deeds. Even today people cele-
brate his victories and sing his praises.

Mohammed Ghory invaded India and attacked Prithviraj's kingdom. But Prithviraj had a stronger army and he
defeated Ghory. Many of Ghory's men were killed and
many others ran for their lives. Ghory himself was
taken prisoner and was brought before Prithviraj. Prithviraj
treated him with respect and allowed him to go free.

Mohammed Ghory went back but only to come again
with a bigger army. He again attacked Prithviraj's kingdom.
Again there was a big battle and again Ghory was defeated
and taken prisoner. Prithviraj admonished him but set him
free once more.

Ghory was determined to take the rich and prosperous
kingdom of Prithviraj Chauhan. He gathered more men
and organized a bigger army and again marched on Delhi.
He was defeated, taken prisoner, and set free for the third

time. He tried many more times to take the kingdom of Prithviraj, and each time he was defeated, taken prisoner, and set free.

Prithviraj was warned by his friends that such an enemy should be completely annihilated, otherwise it would lead to great danger. But he would only reply that he was confident of his strength and he could depend on his men. He did not like killing a person in cold blood.

But there were differences of opinion among his own people on the policy of Prithviraj Chauhan.

Mohammed Ghory came yet once more, and this time with a far greater force. He sensed that there were differences of opinion among Prithviraj's men. He marched on

to Delhi. A huge battle was fought between him and Prithviraj. Prithviraj fought with great courage but he was defeated. He was taken prisoner along with many of his people.

Mohammed Ghory en-throned himself as the Sultan of Delhi. He ordered all the prisoners to be beheaded ex-cept Prithviraj and Chand Bardai, the court poet. Prith-viraj was blinded and put in prison.

Ghory had heard some of Chand's poetry and wanted to be entertained by him. One day Ghory was listening to Chand's recitations in which he sang of the many great qualities of Prithviraj. One composition described how Prithviraj went out hunting and shot a wild animal without even seeing it, guided by the sound that it made. Prithvi-

raj was known as 'shabd bhedi', that is one who could hit a target without seeing it, merely on the direction of the sound.

This was something that Ghory could not believe. He
wanted to see it done. He met Prithviraj in the prison and
asked him to show his skill, just for the pleasure. Prithviraj
refused to oblige him. Ghory then asked Chand to use his
influence on his former master and persuade him to show
how he could shoot at an object without seeing it.

Chand went to Prithviraj and told him of Ghory's
desire. Prithviraj was astonished that Chand, his friend,
should try to please Ghory. But Chand explained to him

that it was a great chance which they could not afford to miss. They could now take revenge on Ghory. Chand and Prithviraj together worked out a plan of action.

Ghory was then informed that Prithviraj had at last agreed to demonstrate his art of shooting.

A day was fixed for the event. Ghory called his durbar to witness Prithviraj's feat. When all had assembled, the blind Prithviraj was brought in. He stood at a distance from the throne where Ghory was seated.

Then Ghory ordered a goat to be brought in and tied to a post at a spot far away from the dais. The goat must be made to bleat, he said, so that Prithviraj would know where it was.

Prithviraj listened as Ghory gave his instructions. Now he knew the exact position of the Sultan on his throne.

Then Chand recited a poem, praising Prithviraj and describing how he could shoot at a target without seeing it, guided by the sound it made.

He concluded his poem by saying that the great Sultan was sitting on his throne as before, eagerly waiting to see the great feat.

At that moment the goat bleated. Prithviraj raised his bow. He took quick aim and shot a sharp arrow not at the goat but at the Sultan. The arrow struck Ghory in the heart and he fell down dead.

In a split second Chand rushed to Prithviraj and cut off his head. And, at the same moment, Chand was killed by Prithviraj's sword before his headless body fell to the ground.

Thus Prithviraj and Chand carried out their plan, and Ghory's men could not do anything either to Prithviraj or to Chand.

THE QAZI'S JUDGEMENT

Sultan Giasuddin was a famous Pathan king who ruled over eastern India. One day, while he was hunting, one of his arrows killed a little boy. The boy was the only son of a poor widow. Crying and wailing, the woman reported the matter to the magistrate, who was known as the Qazi.

The Qazi was in a dilemma. If he accepted the case, he would have to punish the king. If he did not accept it, he would be committing a sin before God. After thinking deeply about it, the Qazi decided to accept

the complaint, and he asked the widow to be present in the court the next day.

Then the Qazi had to summon the Sultan. But to do this he had to find a messenger. He asked one of his assistants to go and give the message to the Sultan.

The assistant began to tremble. If he ignored the Qazi's order, he would be punished. On the other hand, if he summoned the Sultan, he might lose his head.

He thought and thought what to do, and at last he went and stood outside the Sultan's palace. He did not have the courage to go in. What could he do ? He wanted to return, but then the Qazi would dismiss him. At last he thought of a plan. In a loud voice he uttered the call to prayer, the azan, which was usually only made at prayer-time.

Hearing the untimely call to prayer, the Sultan ordered

that the man who had made it should be brought to him. Trembling with fear, the messenger faced the Sultan. The Sultan asked him the cause of his untimely azan. With folded hands the messenger said : "O Lord, forgive me, I have to do my duty. The Qazi has sent me to summon you to his court. You are to appear before him tomorrow morning. I was afraid to come straight to you so I said the call to prayer to attract your attention."

The Sultan was rather pleased with the messenger. He said he would appear before the Qazi the next day at the appointed time.

Accordingly, the next morning the Sultan
was on his way to the Qazi. He had a sharp
sword hidden under his robe.

The Qazi was holding his court. The room
was packed with people, all eager to hear a case
against the Sultan of the country.

Sultan Giasuddin entered. Everybody stood

up, but not the Qazi. He remained sitting as before. The Qazi called the widow and asked her to explain her case. She described what had happened.

The Qazi then said, "Sultan, you killed with your arrow the only son of this widow. You are accused of the crime of killing a poor woman's child. It is a great loss for her and I order you to make good her loss."

The Sultan at once apologized to the widow and arranged to give her gold and gems so that she could live above all want.

When the case was over, the Qazi rose from his chair and offered his seat to the Sultan with due honour.

The Sultan said : " Qazi, had you faltered in your judgement because I was the accused, I would have beheaded you with this sword."

And Giasuddin brought out the sharp weapon from under his robe.

Bowing his head, the Qazi said, " Sir, if you had disobeyed my order, I would have flayed the skin off your back with this whip."

And he took out a knotted leather lash from under his cloak.

" Thanks be to God, we both fulfilled our duty," he said.

The Sultan was very pleased and he embraced his fearless Qazi. Then the whole crowd shouted in their honour.

THE STORY OF GOH

Vallabhi was a famous city in Saurashtra. It was the capital of Siladitya, a famous king of the Surya dynasty.

Siladitya was a mighty ruler. He took possession of many neighbouring kingdoms and added them to his own. Many other kings accepted his supremacy and paid tribute to him.

Siladitya was noble, kind, and good. He ruled his people well. There was peace and prosperity everywhere. Vallabhi was a very rich city. Many invaders had their

eyes on Vallabhi and the Tartars were waiting for an opportunity to attack the city.

Siladitya had a noble and beautiful queen, Pushpavati. A son was born to her, and the people rejoiced. The whole city was gay and happy, and there were feasts and merry-making throughout the night.

But the Tartars were in league with some of the ministers and the commander-in-chief of King Siladitya. The corrupt ministers and officers had been heavily bribed and they had agreed to betray their ruler.

Then, while the city was celebrating the birth of the prince, the Tartars invaded the city. Siladitya put up a

great and heroic battle but he was defeated with the help of his own people. Siladitya was killed and the city was looted and razed to the ground.

Queen Pushpavati escaped with the baby, her trusted maid, Kamala, and a few others. They took shelter in a temple. But they knew that they were not safe there, as the invaders were not far from the temple and were searching for the queen and the little prince.

All the queen's followers left her, except Kamala. The queen and Kamala then decided to leave the temple. At dead of night they silently crept away and went and took shelter in a far-off cave. And there they stayed, the queen, Kamala, and the baby prince.

But Queen Pushpavati could not bear the loss of her husband, and she fell ill. As time passed, she grew worse

and worse, and the day came when, sorrowfully, she handed the little prince to Kamala, and, begging her to look after him, she breathed her last.

Kamala was in deep sorrow. But she was a brave woman, and she decided that she would bring up the prince with every care. She could not do so if she stayed in the cave, so she decided to go to her parents.

The journey to her father's house was long and difficult. She was afraid to travel during the day as some enemy might identify her and the little prince. So she travelled only at night and hid herself during the day.

After a tiring journey which lasted for many days, she reached her parents' house in Birnagar. There she brought up the young prince. She acted as his mother and gave him all the education and training she could afford. She called him Goh.

Birnagar was on the edge of the Bhil country. As Goh grew up, he had many young Bhil boys as friends and playmates.

He grew up into an adventurous boy. He went hunting in the thick jungle with the Bhil boys. Goh was the best hunter among them and the boys looked upon him as their leader.

Mandlik was the Bhil chieftain of this forest region. The Bhil kingdom had been under the supremacy of King Siladitya, and Mandlik had recognized him as a great ruler and had respected him very much. When Siladitya died, Mandlik became independent. But he was always willing to recognize the rightful successor.

It was the day of the Bhil annual festival. The Bhils celebrated the day by feasting and dancing.

That day Goh and his friends went out hunting in the thick jungle. A fierce boar suddenly charged at Goh. He was so clever and brave that he not only avoided the boar but he pierced its neck with a sharp lance. Then, jumping on its back, he stabbed the boar with his dagger until it fell down dead. All the boys danced with joy at their leader's brave deed. They embraced him and showered flowers on him. The boys then wanted to carry the boar to their chieftain, Mandlik, as a gift on this festival day. Goh agreed. The boys carried the enormous boar to their chieftain, and Goh went with them.

Mandlik sat on a huge stone throne and the Bhils had gathered round him in the open. Music was being played and men and women were dancing. The boar was

presented to the chieftain. He looked at the boar and recognized it as the animal he had tried many times to kill.

"Who killed this big boar?" he asked.

"He did," said a boy, pointing at Goh.

"Who are you and what is your name?" asked Mandlik.

"He is Goh. He is the son of a brahmin living just outside the jungle," said another boy. "He is our friend and we always play and hunt together."

"The son of a brahmin?" Mandlik exclaimed. "How can a brahmin do such a wonderful thing?"

"Yes," said Goh. "I did kill the boar, and I am the son of a brahmin."

Mandlik could not believe it. He noticed an amulet round Goh's neck. It was a custom in those days that as soon as a child was born the mother or father tied an amulet round his neck or waist to ward off all evil. Inside it was placed an inscription giving the date of birth and parentage of the child. Pushpavati had tied such an amulet round her child's neck.

"Take off that amulet and give it to me. I want to see it," said Mandlik.

"No, I won't!" shouted Goh.

Then Mandlik ordered his men to remove the amulet. Goh felt that they were insulting him and he began to fight everyone who approached him. But he was helpless against so many and the amulet was soon removed. Mandlik opened it and read the inscription which was inside. Now he knew who the boy was.

The Bhil chieftain's joy knew no bounds. He at once took Goh on his lap and embraced him. Tears of happiness rolled down his cheeks. He had found his king, the successor of his noble master Siladitya. He placed the boy on the stone throne and put a crown of flowers on his head.

He loudly proclaimed that the boy was their king and all were to pay homage to him.

Kamala and her father heard what had happened and rushed to the place. There they found the boy crowned the King of the Bhils.

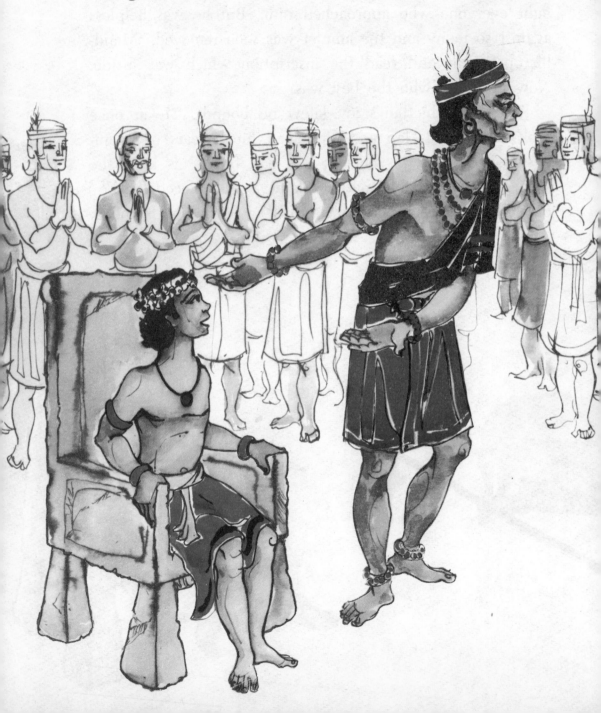